THE ECLECTIC READERS

美国语文读本

WILLIAM H. MCGUFFEY

上海三联书店

图书在版编目（CIP）数据

美国语文读本(第1册) / (美) 麦加菲(McGuffey, W. H.)编.
—上海：上海三联书店，2011.1
ISBN 978-7-5426-3412-2

Ⅰ.①美… Ⅱ.①麦… Ⅲ.①英语–阅读教学–中小学–美国
–课外读物 Ⅳ.①G634.413

中国版本图书馆 CIP 数据核字（2010）第 239796 号

美国语文读本（第 1 册）

编　　　者/ （美）威廉·H·麦加菲

责 任 编 辑/ 黄 韬
装 帧 设 计/ 子木工作室
监　　　制/ 研 发

出 版 发 行/ 上海三联书店
　　　　　　 (200031)中国上海市乌鲁木齐南路 396 弄 10 号
　　　　　　 http: // www.sanlianc. com
　　　　　　 E–mail: shsanlian@yahoo. com.cn
印　　　刷/ 北京领先印刷有限公司

版　　　次/ 2011 年 1 月第 1 版
印　　　次/ 2012 年12月第 3 次印刷
开　　　本/ 640×940 毫米　1/16
字　　　数/ 180 千字
印　　　张/ 10

ISBN 978-7-5426-3412-2/G·1061

定价: 16.00 元

THE ALPHABET

A	a		N	n
B	b		O	o
C	c		P	p
D	d		Q	q
E	e		R	r
F	f		S	s
G	g		T	t
H	h		U	u
I	i		V	v
J	j		W	w
K	k		X	x
L	l		Y	y
M	m		Z	z

Script Alphabet

A B C D E F G

H I J K L M N

O P Q R S T U

V W X Y Z

a b c d e f g h i

j k l m n o p q

r s t u v w x y z

SCRIPT FIGURES

1 2 3 4 5 6 7 8 9 0

出 版 前 言

　　呈现于读者面前的这套《美国语文读本》，亦名《麦加菲读本》，其编者威廉·H·麦加菲曾先后任美国迈阿密大学语言学教授和俄亥俄大学校长。考虑到"麦加菲"在美国已是注册商标，加之它是一套在美国影响深远而广泛的语文课本，我们在中国首次原文出版这套著名教材时，便将书名定为《美国语文读本》。对当今中国读者来讲，这套书既有教材功能，亦是一套提高英语水平的有效读物。

　　《美国语文读本》从19世纪中期至20世纪中叶，一直被广泛用作美国学校的语文教材，据称有10000多所美国学校使用。美国著名汽车制造商亨利·福特称赞这套书是他儿童时代最有兴趣的读物，后来他自费大量印刷这套书，分发给很多学校。21世纪的今天，西方一些私立学校和家庭学校（Homeschool）仍用它作为教材，足见这套书的价值与魅力。据估计，这套书从问世至1960年，至少发行了1.22亿册；1961年后，在西方每年销量仍达30000册以上。应该说，没有哪一套个人主编的教材能超过此发行量了！

　　这套读本的英文原版共分七级，包括启蒙读本和第1-6级。考虑到启蒙读本与第一级篇幅都较少，难易程度也很接近，于是我们将之合并为第1册，其余2-6级与英文原版相同。这样国内出版的这套读本共包括6册。第1册从字母表开始，主要侧重于字母的发音与书写、基本单词与常用句型，同时强调英文书写，课文后面附有不少书法练习，让中国孩子不仅将英语说得像外国人，而且写得也跟外国人一样，这也许是国内英语教学所缺少的一个环节。从第2册开始，均是蕴涵特定主题与思想的课文，每一课包括词汇和课文，对一些难词有英文解释，让学生学会通过简单英文理解生词，养成用英语理解和思维的习惯。第4册还附有课后思考练习，这些练习可以帮助学生更好理解文章，引发孩子们的思考。第5册和第6册的课文前增加了作者简介与相关背景知识，内容丰富而有一定深度。

从所选课文的英文难易程度来看，大致而言，这套读本的第1-3册跟国内小学毕业程度相近，那么第4级以上则适用于中学以上的学习者阅读使用。从文体方面，除了常用文体外，这套读本对诗歌、戏剧、论说文等文体也很重视，书中选取了不少名家的名作名篇。这对国内孩子们真正感受英语语言的魅力是大有帮助的。

在全社会不断呼吁教育改革的今天，我们将这套优秀的美国读本引进到国内，应该具有一定借鉴意义。它有益于中国孩子在学习英语的同时，了解西方的文学与文化历史，通过英语这门语言工具，开阔自己的视野，打开通往世界的心灵之窗。同时，这套书的字里行间灌输了很多做人的道理和准则，让孩子们在学习英语的同时学会做人，这正是我们出版此套书的内心所愿！

作为此书的出版者，我们最后恳请读者原谅并给予帮助的是，由于此套书出版过程中扫描和编排校对的工作量较大，或许会出现一些错误与不当之处，恳请读者谅解并指正，并帮助我们更加完善此套读本。我们的联系方式为 homeschools@sina.com.，并请访问我们的家庭学校博客：http://blog.sina.com.cn/homeschoolnow

出版者

LESSON 1

a   *and*   *cat*   *rat*

a   *c*   *d*   *n*   *r*   *t*

a rat   *a cat*

A cat   *A rat*

A cat and a rat.

A rat and a cat.

LESSON 2

at   the   ran   has

Ann

h   th   s

the cat   *the rat*

The cat has a rat.

The rat ran at Ann.

Ann has a cat.

The cat ran at the rat.

LESSON 3

Nat   *hat*   *fan*   *can*

f

a fan   *a hat*

Ann and Nat.

Ann has a fan.

Nat has a hat.

Ann can fan Nat.

LESSON 4

man   *cap*

lad   *sat*

1   *m*   *p*   *s*

a   *cap*   *the*   *lad*

A man and a lad.

The man sat; the lad ran.

The man has a hat.

The lad has a cap.

LESSON 5   REVIEW

The cat and the rat ran.

Ann sat, and Nat ran.

A rat ran at Nat.

Can Ann fan the lad?

The man and the lad.

The man has a cap.

The lad has a fan.

Has Ann a hat?

Ann has a hat and a fan.

a   at   rat   sat

can   cap   lad   and

The cat ran. Ann ran.

The man has a hat.

LESSON 6

dog   Rab

fat   Nat's

o   b   g

Nat's cap   a fat dog

Has the lad a dog?

The lad has a fat dog.

The dog has Nat's cap.

Nat and Rab ran.

Rab ran at a cat.

LESSON 7

see   *sees*   *frog*

on   *log*

e

a log   *the frog*

See the frog on a log.

Rab sees the frog.

Can the frog see Rab?

The frog can see the dog.

Rab ran at the frog.

LESSON 8

it	stand	Ann's
is	lamp	mat
	i	
a mat		the stand

See the lamp! It is on a mat.

The mat is on the stand.

The lamp is Nat's, and the mat is Ann's.

LESSON 9

Tom   *nag*   *not*
him   *catch*   *he*
     his   *ch*

See the nag! It is Tom's nag.

Can Tom catch his nag?

He can not catch him.

The dog ran at the nag, and the nag ran.

LESSON 10 REVIEW

Tom's nag is fat; his dog is not fat.

Nat is on Tom's nag.

Nat's dog, Rab, can not catch the rat.

See the frog on the log.

A lad sees the frog.

The lad can not catch it.

A cat is on the mat; the cat sees a rat.

Ann's fan is on the stand.

The man has a lamp.

A dog ran at the man.

Ann sat on a log.

Tom sees Nat's dog.

A fat frog is on the log.

Can not Rab catch it ?

LESSON 11

nest   this   eggs she

in   get

box   hen

e   x   sh

the box   a nest

This is a fat hen.

The hen has a nest in the box.

She has eggs in the nest.

A cat sees the nest, and can get the eggs.

LESSON 12

old

run

fox

o   u

Can this old fox catch the hen?

The fox can catch the hen, and get the eggs in the nest.

Run, Rab, and catch the fox.

This nest has eggs in it.

LESSON 13

pond *ducks* *them* *feed*

Nell

I

by

will

i *y* *ck* *w*

Nell is by the pond.

I see ducks on the pond.

Nell sees the ducks, and will feed them.

She can not get the ducks.

LESSON 14

holds   to

blind   Mary

hand   kind

a   o   k   y

This old man can not see. He is blind.

Mary holds him by the hand.

She is kind to the old blind man.

LESSON 15   REVIEW

I see ducks on the pond;

Tom will feed them.

Tom is blind;

he holds a box in his hand.

Nell is kind to him.

This old hen has a nest.

Mary will run and get the eggs.

Sue   doll   dress   new   her

let

e

u

ew

Sue has a doll.

It has a new dress.

She will let Ann hold the doll in her hands, and Ann will fan it.

Sue is kind to Ann.

LESSON 17

there

five *bird*

tree *rob* *do*

e *i* *v*

A bird is in the tree. It has a nest there.

The nest has five eggs in it.

Do not rob the nest.

Will the bird let the cat get her five eggs?

LESSON 18

cage

pet

sing

lives

so

loves

o

g

ng

This is a pet bird.

It lives in a new cage.

It will stand on Sue's hand, and sing.

Sue loves her pet bird.

So do I love it.

LESSON 19

are   you   yes   fast   too

like   boys   of   play

Do you see the boys at play?

Yes, I see them; there are five of them.

Tom is too fat to run fast.

Nat can catch him.

I like to see boys play.

Sue has a doll and a pet bird.

Her doll has a new dress and a cap.

Sue loves Mary, and will let her hold the doll.

The pet bird lives in a cage. Sue and Mary will stand by the cage, and the bird will sing.

There are birds in the tree by the pond. Can you see them?

Yes; there are five of them in a nest.

Tom will not rob a bird's nest. He is too kind to do so.

Nell will feed the ducks.

Sue has a new dress.

LESSON 21

what   night

owl   day

an   but

well   big

eyes   best

a   ow   wh

What bird is this?

It is an owl.

What big eyes it has!

Yes, but it can not see well by day.

The owl can see best at night.

Nat Pond has a pet owl.

LESSON 22

grass *they* *come* *off* *barn*
shade *hot*
cows *our*

e   ou

The day is hot.

The cows are in the shade of the big tree.

They feed on the new grass.

Our cows do not run off.

At night they come to the barn.

LESSON 23

soon   *sun*

neck   *set*

way   *bell*   *one*   *their*

oo

The sun will soon set.

The cows are on their way to the barn.

One old cow has a bell on her neck. She sees our dog, but she will not run.

Our dog is kind to the cows.

LESSON 24

brave　　*if*　　*ship*　　*boat*

drown　*men*　　*rock*　　*save*

The ship has run on a rock.

Five men are on the ship.

If the boat can not get to them, they will drown.

The boat has brave men in it. They will save the five men.

LESSON 25 REVIEW

Come, boys, and feed the cows. The sun has set, and they are at the barn.

Sue has a bell on the neck of her pet cat.

One hot day Ann and Nell sat on the grass in the shade of a big tree. They like to rock their dolls, and sing to them.

The brave men in our boat are on their way to the ship. They will save the men in the ship, if they can. They will not let them drown.

What bird has big eyes? The owl. Can an owl see at night? Yes, an owl can see best at night.

LESSON 26

fall   *ice*   *skates*   *cry*

with   *had*   *stone*   *did*

a   *c*   *sk*

The boys are on the ice with their skates.

There is a stone on the ice.

One boy did not see it, and has had a fall.

But he is a brave boy, and will not cry.

LESSON 27

look	*go*	*John*
here	*all*	*wheel*
mill	*have*	*round*
	oo	*j*

Look! there are John and Sue by the mill pond.

They like to see the big wheel go round.

They have come to play on the logs and in the
boat.

John and Sue will play here all day.

The cows like grass.
They stand in the shade.

LESSON 28

or	*Jane*	*girls*	*floor*
roll	*some*	*which*	*black*

o

Here are some girls with skates; but they are not on the ice.

Their skates roll on the floor.

Which way do you like to skate,—on the ice, or on the floor?

The girl with the new black dress is Jane Bell.

for   *out*   *as*   *how*   *try*

horse   *should*   *hurt*   *cars*   *be*

o   *no*   *u*

Look out for the cars! How fast they come!

No horse can go as fast as the cars.

I will not try to catch them, for I should fall and be hurt.

See the horse look at the cars.

Will he not run?

LESSON 30   REVIEW

There is ice on the pond, and the mill wheel can not go round.

The boys are all out on the ice with their skates.

I will let you and Tom try to skate; but do not fall, for you will be hurt.

Look! here come the cars.

John and Nat try to skate as fast as the cars go, but they can not. John has had a fall.

The girls are not on the pond; but some of them have skates which roll on the floor.

How fast the cars go!
Can you see them?

LESSON 31

work   ax   pile   Ned   think

wood   saw

hard   cut

o   th   n

Ned and John are hard at work.

John has a saw, and Ned has an ax.

They will try to cut all of the wood which you see in the pile.

Do you think they can do this in one day?

LESSON 32

noise   air   hear

gone   May   walk

cool   two

a   oi

Two girls have gone out for a walk.

It is May, and the air is cool. They hear the birds sing in the trees, and they hear the noise of the frogs in the pond.

They see men at work and boys at play.

LESSON 33

pull   cart   goats   Bess
up   ride   hill

u

Bess has a cart and two goats.

She likes to ride in her cart.

See how the goats pull!

Bess is so big, I think she should walk up the
hill.

The goats love Bess, for she feeds them, and is
kind to them.

LESSON 34

blaze   put   yet   house

fire

roof

call

ring

we

z

This house is on fire.

Look! the roof is in a blaze.

Run, boys, and ring the bell. Call some men to put out the fire.

We may yet save the house, if we work hard.

LESSON 35   REVIEW

Bess, do you hear a noise?

Yes, Tom; what is it?

It is the mill by our house; logs are cut there.

How do they cut the logs, Tom,—with an ax?

Not with an ax, Bess; it is too hard work; they cut them with a saw.

May we not go and see the mill at work, Tom?

Yes, I think so. The air is cool, and we can walk in the shade. We should go soon, Bess, or the pile of wood will be gone.

Our two goats and the cart are here, Tom; we can ride to the mill. It is not up hill, and the goats can pull us fast.

LESSON 36

Miss *wants* *would* *tells*

rule

keep

good

that

each

u

The girls and boys all love Miss May; she is so kind to them.

Miss May tells them there is a rule that she wants them to keep. It is, "Do to each one as you would like each one to do to you."

This is a good rule, and all boys and girls should keep it.

school   child

church   when

books

slates

What kind of house is this?

Do you think it is a schoolhouse, or a church?

It looks like a church, but I think it is a schoolhouse.

I see the boys and girls with their books and slates.

When the bell rings, they will go in.

A good child likes to go to school.

LESSON 38

quail

seen

me

eat

know

quick

kill

oh

first

Henry

qu

"John! come here. Be quick, and tell me what kind of bird this is."

"Do you not know, Henry?"

"Oh, no! what is it?"

"It is a quail."

"It is the first quail I have seen. Is it good to eat?"

"Yes; but I should not like to kill it."

Kate   *dear*

name   *blue*

baby   *near*

shut   *crib*

sit

Is not this a dear baby in the crib?

Her name is Kate, and she has big, blue eyes. You can not see her eyes, for they are shut.

Kate is a good baby; but she will cry if she is hurt, or if she is not well.

Bess likes to sit near the baby, and to rock her in the crib.

LESSON 40   REVIEW

Henry Black and Ned Bell live near our house. They go to school, and I see them go by each day with their books and slates.

Miss May tells the girls and boys that they should be at the schoolhouse when the bell rings. So Henry walks fast, and is first at school. He is a good boy, and wants to keep the rule of the school.

Ned is not a good boy. I do not think he likes to go to school or to church.

I saw him try to kill a quail with a stone. The quail is too quick a bird for that, and Ned did not hurt it; but I know that a good child would not try to kill a bird.

There is a baby at Ned's house. Her name is Kate. Ned is not a good boy; but he loves Kate, and I do not think he would hurt her.

LESSON 41

light   *far*   *its*   *high*

where   *sea*   *tall*   *were*

The tall house which you see on that high rock is a lighthouse. At night its light is seen far out at sea, and the men on ships can tell where to go.

If it were not for this, they would run on the rocks.

How would you like to live in a lighthouse?

42

LESSON 42

wrong   wolf   us   my   took

sheep   more

watch   lambs

Let us watch the sheep as they feed on the hills. They like to eat the new grass.

Do you see my two lambs? I had two more; but an old wolf took them one night.

I love my pet lambs. It would be wrong to hurt them.

LESSON 43

laugh *snow* *head* *fun*

mouth *made* *pipe*

gh

The boys have made a big snow man.

They have put a tall hat on his head, and an old pipe in his mouth.

Hear them lau*gh* as they play!

It is good fun for the boys.

They would like to have it snow all day and all night.

LESSON 44

sweets   mean

please   bee

buzz   vine

could

said

once

"Buzz! buzz!" a bee said to Mary.

"What do you mean?" said Mary. "Please tell me once more."

"Buzz! buzz! buzz!" but Mary could not tell its wants.

I think it said, "Please let me get some sweets in this vine."

LESSON 45   REVIEW

One day Nat and I sat on the high hill by the sea, where the tall lighthouse stands. We could look far out, and could see the ships at sea.

As we sat there, we saw a man near by, with some sheep and lambs. The man had a pipe in his mouth. He sat with us, and let the sheep eat the grass.

What fun it is to see lambs play! It made us laugh to see them.

The man said that once, when the sheep and lambs were out in the snow, an old wolf took one of the lambs, and ran off with it.

I think that men should watch their sheep, so that a wolf can not catch them.

LESSON 46

while	might	time	things
done	right	your	halves

Work while you work,
 Play while you play;
One thing each time,
 That is the way.

All that you do,
 Do with your might;
Things done by halves.
 Are not done right.

LESSON 47

went

fish

fell

safe

arms

sprang   *was*   *thank*   *got*

One day John went to the pond to fish. His dog, Watch, went with him.

John sat on a log for a time, but did not catch a fish.

As he got up to go, he fell off the log.

Watch sprang in to save him. John put his arms round the dog's neck, and was soon safe on the log once more.

"Thank you, my brave old dog," said John to Watch.

LESSON 48

James   *asks*   *warm*   *town*

then   *drives*   *been*   *show*

James has been to the mill. The day is warm, and he lets his horse stand in the shade.

A girl asks him to show her the way to the town. He tells her the way, and then drives on.

LESSON 49

I'll   *she'll*   *don't*

puss   *pur*

pat   *fur*

harm   *deeds*

I love my dear puss,
   Her fur is so warm;
And, if I don't hurt her,
   She'll do me no harm.

I'll pat my dear puss,
   And then she will pur,
And show me her thanks
   For my kind deeds to her.

LESSON 50

now   wreaths   who   queen

woods   shall   crown

It is the first of May. The boys and girls have
gone to the woods to have a good time. See them
at their play.

The girls have wreaths in their hands.

Now they will crown some one Queen of the
May. Who shall it be?

It should be the best girl, and that is Kate.

LESSON 51

God   small   from
world   moon
shine   nut
long   ago

Do you see that tall tree?

Long ago it sprang up from a small nut.

Do you know who made it do so?

It was God, my child. God made the world and all things in it. He made the sun to light the day, and the moon to shine at night.

God shows that he loves us by all that he has done for us. Should we not then love him?

LESSON 52

Lord   smile   joys   tear   nigh

morn   griefs   woes   stars   say

When the stars, at set of sun,

    Watch you from on high;

When the light of morn has come,

    Think the Lord is nigh.

All you do, and all you say,

    He can see and hear;

When you work and when you play,

    Think the Lord is near.

All your joys and griefs he knows,

    Sees each smile and tear;

When to him you tell your woes,

    Know the Lord will hear.

LESSON 53

dog   *the*   *ran*

a   *o*   *n*   *d*   *g*   *r*   *th*

The dog.

The dog ran.

cat   *mat*   *is*   *on*

c   *t*   *i*   *m*   *s*

the cat   *the mat*

Is the cat on the mat?

The cat is on the mat.

LESSON 55

it	his	pen	hand
a	in	has	man
	p	h	e

The man.   *A pen.*

The man has a pen.

Is the pen in his hand?

It is in his hand.

hen

fat

rat

box

big   run   from   can

f   b   x   u

A fat hen.   *A big rat.*

The fat hen is on the box.

The rat ran from the box.

Can the hen run?

LESSON 57

Rab Ann hat catch see

e ch s

See Rab! See Ann!

See! Rab has the hat.

Can Ann catch Rab?

LESSON 58

she　　　　*pat*　　　　*too*　　　　*now*

let　　　　*me*

sh　　　　*oo*　　　　*ow*　　　　*l*

Ann can catch Rab.

See! *Sh*e has the hat.

N*ow* Ann can pat Rab.

*L*et me pat Rab, *too*.

LESSON 59

Ned   *eggs*   *black*   *left*

fed   *nest*   *them*   *get*

will   *a black hen*   *the nest*

w   *ck*

Ned has fed the hen.

She is a bla*ck* hen.

She has left the nest.

See the eggs in the nest!

Will the hen let Ned get them?

LESSON 60

head   *he*   *Nat*

come   *with*   *and*

o

Let me get the black hat. Now Ned has it on his head, and he is a big man.

Come, Nat, see the big man with his black hat.

pat	catch	has	left
hat	can	black	eggs
Rab	Ann	fed	get

Ned is on the box. He has a pen in his hand. A big rat is in the box. Can the dog catch the rat?

Come with me, Ann, and see the man with a black hat on his head.

The fat hen has left the nest. Run, Nat, and get the eggs.

———————

The cat ran. Ann ran.
The man has a hat.

LESSON 62

Nell	*some*
pan	*him*
yes	*do*
you	*have*
I	*to*
i *y*	*v* *o*

Do you see Nell?

Yes; she has a pan with some eggs in it.

Let me have the pan and the eggs, will you, Nell?

Has the black hen left the nest?

I will now run to catch Rab. Will you run, too?

LESSON 63

O	*whip*	*Ben*
up	*still*	*sit*
if	*stand*	*Jip*
o	*wh*	*j*

O Ben! let me get in, will you?

Yes, if you will sit still.

Stand still, Jip, and let Ann get in.

Now, Ben, hand me the *wh*ip.

Get up, *J*ip!

Kitty
nice
sweet
sing
just
hang
cage
then

song   *pet*   *put*   *not*

k   *g*   *c*   *a*   *y*   *ng*   *u*

Kitty has a nice pet. It can sing a sweet song.

She has just fed it.

She will now put it in the cage, and hang the cage up. Then the cat can not catch it.

Tom   *top*   *Kitty's*

at

back

look

good   *doll*   *think*   *spot*

          th   *n*   *oo*

Look at Tom and his dog. The dog has a black spot on his back. Do you *thin*k he is a good dog?

Tom has a big top, *too*. It is on the box with Kitty's doll.

LESSON 66

sun	*we*	*how*	*pond*
stop	*for*	*go*	*swim*
her	*us*	*hot*	*duck*
	e	*o*	

The sun is up. The man has fed the black hen and the fat duck.

Now the duck will swim in the pond. The hen has run to her nest.

Let us not stop at the pond now, for it is hot.

See how still it is! We will go to see Tom and his top.

LESSON 67

John	*rock*	*set*	*jump*
fun	*must*	*may*	*under*
skip	*bank*	*but*	*touch*

O John! the sun has just set. It is not hot, now.

Let us run and jump. I think it is fun to run, and skip, and jump.

See the duck on the pond! Her nest is up on the bank, under the rock.

We must not touch the nest, but we may look at it.

LESSON 68 REVIEW

The sun has set, and the pond is still.

John, Ned, Ben, Tom, and Nell stand on the bank, and look at the duck.

The dog with a black spot on his back, is with Tom. See! Tom has his hat in his hand. He has left his big top on the box.

Kitty's doll is on the rock.

Nell has put her pet in the cage. It will sing a sweet song. The duck has her nest under the rock.

It is not hot now. Let us run, and skip, and jump on the bank. Do you not think it is fun?

LESSON 69

are   *ink*   *moss*   *this*   *tub*   *upset*

SLATE WORK

The pen and the ink are on the stand.   Is this a good pen?   The moss is on the rock. This duck can swim. Ben upset the tub.

LESSON 70

nut　　*did*　　*shut*　　*shall*　　*lost*　　*fox*

men　　*met*　　*step*　　*into*　　*hunt*　　*mud*

SLATE WORK.

Will the dog hunt a fox ?
Ben lost his hat. Shall I
shut the box ? I met him
on the step. Did you jump
into the mud ? I have a
nut. I met the men.

LESSON 71

Kate	old	no	grass
dear	likes	be	drink
milk	cow	out	gives

a

O Kate! the old cow is in the pond: see her drink! Will she not come out to get some grass?

No, John, she likes to be in the pond. See how still she stands!

The dear old cow gives us sweet milk to drink.

LESSON 72

mamma	*large*	*as*	*papa*
arms	*ride*	*far*	*barn*
both	*Prince*	*trot*	*your*

Papa, will you let me ride with you on Prince? I will sit still in your arms.

See, mamma! We are both on Prince. How large he is!

Get up, Prince! You are not too fat to trot as far as the barn.

LESSON 73

of	*that*	*toss*	*fall*
well	*Fanny*	*ball*	*wall*
was	*pretty*	*done*	*what*

a

O Fanny, what a pretty ball!

Yes; can you catch it, Ann?

Toss it to me, and see. I will not let it fall.

That was well done.

Now, Fanny, toss it to the top of the wall, if you

can.

LESSON 74

had went *call* *might*

flag *near* *swam* *swing*

Did you call us, mamma?

I went with Tom to the pond. I had my doll, and Tom had his flag.

The fat duck swam to the bank, and we fed her.

Did you think we might fall into the pond?

We did not go too near, did we, Tom?

May we go to the swing, now, mamma?

LESSON 75

here	*band*	*hear*	*horse*
play	*they*	*pass*	*where*
front	*fine*	*hope*	*comes*

e

Here comes the band! Shall we call mamma and Fanny to see it?

Let us stand still, and hear the men play as they pass.

I hope they will stop here and play for us.

See the large man in front of the band, with his big hat. What has he in his hand? How fine he looks!

Look, too, at the man on that fine horse.

If the men do not stop, let us go with them and see where they go.

LESSON 76

Bess   happy   make   cart   tent   woods

little   very   bed   Robert   gone   draw

Bess and Robert are very happy; papa and mamma have gone to the woods with them.

Robert has a big tent and a flag, and Bess has a little bed for her doll.

Jip is with them. Robert will make him draw Bess and her doll in the cart.

LESSON 77

James   Mary

made   sang

my   lay

sport   spade

lap   dig

doll's   sand

said

"Kate, will you play with me?" said James. "We will dig in the sand with this little spade. That will be fine sport."

"Not now James" said Kate; "for I must make my doll's bed. Get Mary to play with you."

James went to get Mary to play with him. Then Kate made the doll's bed.

She sang a song to her doll, and the doll lay very still in her lap.

Did the doll hear Kate sing?

LESSON 78

its   *shade*   *brook*   *picks*   *all*

by   *help*   *stones*   *glad*   *soft*

Kate has left her doll in its little bed, and has gone to play with Mary and James. They are all in the shade, now, by the brook.

James digs in the soft sand with his spade, and Mary picks up little stones and puts them in her lap.

James and Mary are glad to see Kate. She will help them pick up stones and dig, by the little brook.

82

LESSON 79   REVIEW

"What shall we do?" said Fanny to John. "I do not like to sit still. Shall we hunt for eggs in the barn?"

"No" said John; "I like to play on the grass. Will not papa let us catch Prince, and go to the big woods?"

"We can put the tent in the cart, and go to some nice spot where the grass is soft and sweet."

"That will be fine," said Fanny. "I will get my doll, and give her a ride with us."

"Yes," said John, "and we will get mamma to go, too. She will hang up a swing for us in the shade."

LESSON 80

peep   *while*
take   *sleep*

tuck   *safe*   *oh*   *wet*   *feet*

chick   *can't*   *feels*   *wing*

Peep, peep! Where have you gone, little chick? Are you lost? Can't you get back to the hen?

Oh, here you are! I will take you back. Here, hen, take this little chick under your wing.

Now, chick, tuck your little, wet feet under you, and go to sleep for a while.

Peep, peep! How safe the little chick feels now!

LESSON 81

wind	*time*	*there*	*fence*
kite	*high*	*eyes*	*bright*
flies	*why*	*day*	*shines*

This is a fine day. The sun shines bright. There is a good wind, and my kite flies high. I can just see it.

The sun shines in my eyes; I will stand in the

shade of this high fence.

Why, here comes my dog! He was under the cart. Did you see him there?

What a good time we have had! Are you not glad that we did not go to the woods with John?

SLATE WORK

The pond is still. How it shines in the hot sun! Let us go into the woods where we can sit in the shade.

LESSON 82

wish	*float*	*tie*	*know*
rope	*boat*	*try*	*shore*
give	*pole*	*don't*	*push*
drag	*won't*	*oar*	*funny*

"Kate, I wish we had a boat to put the dolls in. Don't you?"

"I know what we can do. We can get the little tub, and tie a rope to it, and drag it to the pond. This will float with the dolls in it, and we can get a pole to push it from the shore."

"What a funny boat, Kate! A tub for a boat, and a pole for an oar! Won't it upset?"

"We can try it, Nell, and see."

"Well you get the tub, and I will get a pole and a rope. We will put both dolls in the tub, and give them a ride."

SLATE WORK

The dolls had a nice ride to the pond. A soft wind made the tub float out. Nell let the pole fall on the tub, and upset it.

LESSON 83

bound   Rose   called   got
drown   found   brave   came

Ponto   jumped   mouth
around   brought   water

"Here, Ponto! Here, Ponto!" Kate called to her dog. "Come, and get the dolls out of the pond."

Rose went under, but she did not drown. Bess was still on the top of the water.

Ponto came with a bound, and jumped into the pond. He swam around, and got Bess in his mouth, and brought her to the shore.

Ponto then found Rose, and brought her out, too.

Kate said, "Good, old Ponto! Brave old dog!"

What do you think of Ponto?

LESSON 84

June	*Lucy's*	*air*	*kind*
trees	*singing*	*blue*	*when*
pure	*says*	*sky*	*picnic*

What a bright June day! The air is pure. The sky is as blue as it can be.

Lucy and her mamma are in the woods. They

have found a nice spot, where there is some grass.

They sit in the shade of the trees, and Lucy is singing.

The trees are not large, but they make a good shade.

Lucy's kind mamma says that they will have a picnic when her papa can get a tent.

LESSON 85 REVIEW

James and Robert have gone into the shade of a high wall to play ball.

Mary and Lucy have come up from the pond near by, with brave old Ponto, to see them play.

When they toss the ball up in the air, and try to catch it, Ponto runs to get it in his mouth.

Now the ball is lost. They all look for it under the trees and in the grass; but they can not see it. Where can it be?

See! Ponto has found it. Here he comes with it. He will lay it at little Lucy's feet, or put it in her hand.

boy	*our*	*spoil*	*hurrah*
own	*coil*	*noise*	*fourth*
such	*join*	*thank*	*about*
hoist	*pay*	*July*	*playing*

"Papa, may we have the big flag?" said James.

"What can my little boy do with such a big flag?"

"Hoist it on our tent, papa. We are playing Fourth of July."

"Is that what all this noise is about? Why not hoist your own flags?"

"Oh! they are too little."

"You might spoil my flag."

"Then we will all join to pay for it. But we will not spoil it, papa."

"Take it, then, and take the coil of rope with it."

"Oh! thank you. Hurrah for the flag, boys!"

LESSON 87

finished   *bonnet*   *lesson*

saved   *white*

away   *I've*

am   *work*

scamper   *ready*   *garden*

THE WHITE KITTEN.

Kitty, my pretty, white kitty,
   Why do you scamper away?
I've finished my work and my lesson,
   And now I am ready for play.

Come, kitty, my own little kitty,
   I've saved you some milk come and see;
Now drink while I put on my bonnet,
   And play in the garden with me.

LESSON 88

care   always   line   Frank

row   been   keeps   home

Frank has a pretty boat. It is white, with a black line near the water.

He keeps it in the pond, near his home. He always takes good care of it.

Frank has been at work in the garden, and will now row a while.

LESSON 89

much	*one*	*yet*	*hungry*
seen	*grandma*	*corn*	*would*

"What is that?" said Lucy, as she came out on the steps. "Oh, it is a little boat! What a pretty one it is!"

"I will give it to you when it is finished," said John, kindly. "Would you like to have it?"

"Yes, very much, thank you, John. Has grandma seen it?"

"Not yet; we will take it to her by and by. What have you in your pan, Lucy?"

"Some corn for my hens, John; they must be very hungry by this time."

market

basket

bread

bought

meat

tea

trying

tell

which

James has been to market with his mamma.

She has bought some bread, some meat, and some tea, which are in the basket on her arm.

James is trying to tell his mamma what he has seen in the market.

LESSON 91

reads   so   wears   please

could hair

fast   love

easy   gray

chair   who

glasses

See my dear, old grandma in her easy-chair!
How gray her hair is! She wears glasses when she
reads.

She is always kind, and takes such good care of
me that I like to do what she tells me.

When she says, "Robert, will you get me a drink?" I run as fast as I can to get it for her. Then she says, "Thank you, my boy."

Would you not love a dear, good grandma, who is so kind? And would you not do all you could to please her?

LESSON 92

does   *wonder*   *mother*   *other*

bee   *honey*   *listen*   *flower*

"Come here, Lucy, and listen! What is in this flower?"

"O mother! it is a bee. I wonder how it came to be shut up in the flower!"

"It went into the flower for some honey, and it may be it went to sleep. Then the flower shut it in.

"The bee likes honey as well as we do, but it does not like to be shut up in the flower.

"Shall we let it out, Lucy?"

"Yes; then it can go to other flowers, and get honey."

LESSON 93

best	*hitched*	*their*	*should*
or	*riding*	*live*	*holds*
hay	*driving*	*tight*	*early*

Here come Frank and James White. Do you know where they live?

Frank is riding a horse, and James is driving one hitched to a cart. They are out very early in the day. How happy they are!

See how well Frank rides, and how tight James holds the lines!

The boys should be kind to their horses. It is not best to whip them.

When they have done riding, they will give the horses some hay or corn.

SLATE WORK

Some horses can trot very fast. Would you like to ride fast? One day I saw a dog hitched to a little cart. The cart had some corn in it.

LESSON 94

looking   *thought*   *picking*

heard   *chirp*

were   *told*

search   *dearly*

young   *girl*

loved   *birds*

children   *besides*

A little girl went in search of flowers for her mother. It was early in the day, and the grass was wet. Sweet little birds were singing all around her.

And what do you think she found besides flowers? A nest with young birds in it.

While she was looking at them, she heard the mother bird chirp, as if she said, "Do not touch my children, little girl, for I love them dearly."

The little girl now thought how dearly her own

mother loved her.

So she left the birds. Then picking some flowers, she went home, and told her mother what she had seen and heard.

LESSON 95

eight	*ask*	*after*	*town*
past	*ticket*	*right*	*half*
two	*train*	*ding*	*lightning*

"Mamma, will you go to town?"

"What do you ask for a ticket on your train?"

"Oh! we will give you a ticket, mamma."

"About what time will you get back? "

"At half past eight."

"Ah! that is after bedtime. Is this the fast train?"

"Yes, this is the lightning train."

"Oh! that is too fast for me."

"What shall we get for you in town, mamma?"

"A big basket, with two good little children in it."

"All right! Time is up! Ding, ding!"

LESSON 96

school   *even*   *three*

room   *small*

book   *teacher*   *noon*

rude   *reading*   *poor*

It is noon, and the school is out. Do you see the children at play? Some run and jump, some play ball, and three little girls play school under a tree.

What a big room for such a small school!

Mary is the teacher. They all have books in their hands, and Fanny is reading.

They are all good girls, and would not be rude even in playing school.

Kate and Mary listen to Fanny as she reads from her book.

What do you think she is reading about? I will tell you. It is about a poor little boy who was lost in the woods.

When Fanny has finished, the three girls will go home.

In a little while, too, the boys will give up their playing.

apple	mew	tease	cracker
down	new	silly	asleep
wants	calls	knew	friends
upon	flew	Poll	Polly

Lucy has a new pet. Do you know what kind of bird it is? Lucy calls her Polly.

Polly can say, "Poor Poll! Poor Poll! Polly wants a cracker;" and she can mew like a cat.

But Polly and the cat are not good friends. One day Polly flew down, and lit upon the cat's back when she was asleep.

I think she knew the cat would not like that, and she did it to tease her.

When Lucy pets the cat, Polly flies up into the old apple tree, and will not come when she calls her. Then Lucy says, "What a silly bird!"

"Well, children, did you have a nice time in the woods?"

"Oh yes, mother, such a good time! See what sweet flowers we found, and what soft moss. The best flowers are for grandma. Won't they please her?"

"Yes; and it will please grandma to know that you thought of her."

"Rab was such a good dog, mother.

We left him under the big tree by the brook, to take care of the dolls and the basket.

"When we came back, they were all safe. No one could get them while Rab was there. We gave him some of the crackers from the basket.

"O mother, how the birds did sing in the woods!

"Fanny said she would like to be a bird, and have a nest in a tree. But I think she would want to come home to sleep."

"If she were a bird, her nest would be her home. But what would mother do, I wonder, without her little Fanny?"

LESSON 99

beach	*shells*	*these*	*seat*
waves	*going*	*ever*	*sea*
watch	*evening*	*lazy*	*side*

These boys and girls live near the sea. They have been to the beach. It is now evening, and they are going home.

John, who sits on the front seat, found some

pretty shells. They are in the basket by his side.

Ben White is driving. He holds the lines in one hand, and his whip in the other.

Robert has his hat in his hand, and is looking at the horses. He thinks they are very lazy; they do not trot fast.

The children are not far from home. In a little while the sun will set, and it will be bedtime.

Have you ever been at the seaside? Is it not good sport to watch the big waves, and to play on the wet sand?

LESSON 100

log　　　*quiet*　　　*proud*　　　*pulled*

fish　　　*stump*　　　*river*　　　*father*

One evening Frank's father said to him, "Frank, would you like to go with me to catch some fish?"

"Yes; may I go? and with you, father? "

"Yes, Frank, with me."

"Oh, how glad I am!"

Here they are, on the bank of a river. Frank has

just pulled a fine fish out of the water. How proud he feels!

See what a nice, quiet spot they have found. Frank has the stump of a big tree for his seat, and his father sits on a log near by. They like the sport.

LESSON 101

rain	*outside*	*often*	*pitter*
say	*window*	*sound*	*patter*
drops	*sometimes*	*only*	*music*

SLATE WORK

I wish, Mamma you would tell me where the rain comes from. Does it come from the sky? And when the little drops pitter-patter on the window do you think they are playing with me? I can not work or read, for I love to listen to them. I often think their sound is pretty music. But the rain keeps children at home and sometimes I do not like that; then,

The little raindrops only say,
"Pit, pitter, patter, pat;
While we play on the out-side,
Why can't you play on that?"

LESSON 102

sled   *throw*   *winter*   *hurt*

ice   *cover*   *Henry*   *next*

skate   *ground*   *merry*   *snow*

sister *laughing*   *hope*   *pair*

I like winter, when snow and ice cover the ground. What fun it is to throw snowballs, and to skate on the ice!

See the boys and girls! How merry they are!

Henry has his sled, and draws his little sister. There they go!

I think Henry is kind, for his sister is too small to skate.

Look! Did you see that boy fall down? But I see he is not hurt, for he is laughing.

Some other boys have just come to join in the sport. See them put on their skates.

Henry says, that he hopes his father will get a pair of skates for his sister next winter.

paw	*polite*
means	*isn't*
speak	*sir*
shake	*Fido*
tricks	*teach*
	dinner
	Ellen
	bowwow

Ellen, do look at Fido! He sits up in a chair, with my hat on. He looks like a little boy; but it is only Fido.

Now see him shake hands. Give me your paw, Fido. How do you do, sir? Will you take dinner with us. Fido? Speak!

Fido says, "Bowwow," which means, "Thank you, I will."

Isn't Fido a good dog, Ellen? He is always so polite.

When school is out, I will try to teach him some other tricks.

puss   shed

pain   way

stole   saw

hid   eat

Hattie

suffer

sorry

something   caught   tried   Nero

"O Hattie! I just saw a large rat in the shed; and old Nero tried to catch it."

"Did he catch it, Frank?"

"No; Nero did not; but the old cat did."

"My cat?"

"No, it was the other one."

"Do tell me how she got it, Frank. Did she run after it?"

"No, that was not the way. Puss was hid on a big box. The rat stole out, and she jumped at it and caught it."

"Poor rat! It must have been very hungry; it came out to get something to eat."

"Why, Hattie, you are not sorry puss got the rat, are you?"

"No, I can not say I am sorry she got it; but I do not like to see even a rat suffer pain."

LESSON 105

roll	*build*	*grandpa*	*hard*
foam	*ships*	*houses*	*long*
sail	*break*	*wooden*	*blow*

Mary and Lucy have come down to the beach with their grandpa. They live in a town near the sea.

Their grandpa likes to sit on the large rock, and watch the big ships as they sail far away on the blue sea. Sometimes he sits there all day long.

The little girls like to dig in the sand, and pick up pretty shells. They watch the waves as they roll up on the beach, and break into white foam.

They sometimes make little houses of sand, and build walls around them; and they dig wells with their small wooden spades.

They have been picking up shells for their little sister. She is too young to come to the beach.

I think all children like to play by the seaside when the sun is bright, and the wind does not blow too hard.

asked   wanted

four   Willie's

night   rabbits

lad   carried

cents   telling

fifty   master

One day, Willie's father saw a boy at the market with four little white rabbits in a basket.

He thought these would be nice pets for Willie; so he asked the lad how much he wanted for his rabbits.

The boy said, "Only fifty cents, sir."

Willie's father bought them, and carried them home.

Here you see the rabbits and their little master.

He has a pen for them, and always shuts them in it at night to keep them safe.

He gives them bread and grass to eat. They like grass, and will take it from his hand. He has called in a little friend to see them.

Willie is telling him about their funny ways.

SLATE WORK

Some rabbits are as white as snow, some are black, and others have white and black spots. What soft, kind eyes they have!

LESSON 107

bush	*cunning*	*place*	*show*
find	*broken*	*over*	*bring*
again			*fasten*

"Come here, Rose. Look down into this bush."

"O Willie! a bird's nest! What cunning, little eggs! May we take it, and show it to mother?"

"What would the old bird do, Rose, if she should come back and not find her nest?"

"Oh, we would bring it right back, Willie!"

"Yes; but we could not fasten it in its place again. If the wind should blow it over, the eggs would get broken."

LESSON 108

strong   *round*   *dry*   *bill*   *worked*

sends   *claws*   *flit*   *God*   *spring*

"How does the bird make the nest so strong, Willie?"

"The mother bird has her bill and her claws to work with, but she would not know how to make the nest if God did not teach her. Do you see what it is made of?"

"Yes, Willie, I see some horse-hairs and some dry grass. The old bird must have worked hard to find all the hairs, and make them into such a pretty, round nest."

"Shall we take the nest, Rose?"

"Oh no, Willie! We must not take it; but we will come and look at it again, some time."

God made the little birds to sing.
And flit from tree to tree;
Tis He who sends them in the spring
To sing for you and me.

feathers   ago   fly   worm   crumb

feeding   ugly   off   feed   brown

guess   things

"Willie, when I was feeding the birds just now, a little brown bird flew away with a crumb in its bill."

"Where did it go, Rose?"

"I don't know; away off, somewhere."

"I can guess where, Rose. Don't you know the nest we saw some days ago? What do you think is in it now?"

"O Willie, I know! Some little brown birds. Let us go and see them."

"All right; but we must not go too near. There! I just saw the old bird fly out of the bush. Stand here, Rose. Can you see?"

"Why, Willie, what ugly little things! What big mouths they have, and no feathers!"

"Keep still, Rose. Here comes the old bird with a worm in her bill. How hard she must work to feed them all!"

LESSON 110

falling	counts	woes	nigh
begun	griefs	stars	tear
morning	Lord	each	joys

When the stars at set of sun
   Watch you from on high,
When the morning has begun,
   Think the Lord is nigh.

All you do and all you say,
   He can see and hear:
When you work and when you play,
   Think the Lord is near.

All your joys and griefs He knows,
   Counts each falling tear,
When to Him you tell your woes,
   Know the Lord will hear.

LESSON 111

| whistle | basket |
| pocket | willow |

note	filled	dead	sick
walk	every	blew	lane
lame	taking	cane	took

One day, when Mary was taking a walk down the lane, trying to sing her doll to sleep, she met Frank, with his basket and cane.

Frank was a poor, little, lame boy. His father and mother were dead. His dear, old grandma took care of him, and tried to make him happy.

Every day, Mary's mother filled Frank's basket with bread and meat, and a little tea for his grandma.

"How do you do, Frank?" said Mary. "Don't make a noise; my doll is going to sleep. It is just a little sick to-day."

"Well, then, let us whistle it to sleep." And Frank, taking a willow whistle out of his pocket, blew a long note.

"Oh, how sweet!" cried Mary. "Do let me try."

LESSON 112

turned   *face*   *cried*   *low*

almost   *soon*   *more*   *cry*

once   *because*

"Yes, Mary, I will give it to you, because you are so good to my grandma."

"Oh! thank you very much." Mary blew and blew a long time. "I can't make it whistle," said

she, almost ready to cry.

"Sometimes they will whistle, and sometimes they won't," said Frank. "Try again, Mary."

She tried once more, and the whistle made a low, sweet sound. "It whistles!" she cried.

In her joy, she had turned the doll's face down, and its eyes shut tight, as if it had gone to sleep.

"There!" cried Frank, "I told you the way to put a doll to sleep, is to whistle to it."

"So it is," said Mary. "Dear, little thing; it must be put in its bed now."

So they went into the house. Frank's basket was soon filled, and he went home happy.

stood	himself	flapping	first
twelve	flapped	walked	flap
obey	better	Chippy	food
stone	before	chickens	kept

There was once a big, white hen that had twelve little chickens. They were very small, and the old hen took good care of them. She found food for them in the daytime, and at night kept them under her wings.

One day, this old hen took her chickens down to a small brook. She thought the air from the water would do them good.

When they got to the brook, they walked on the bank a little while. It was very pretty on the other side of the brook, and the old hen thought she would take her children over there.

There was a large stone in the brook: she thought it would be easy for them to jump to that stone, and from it to the other side.

So she jumped to the stone, and told the children to come after her. For the first time, she found that they would not obey her.

She flapped her wings, and cried, "Come here, all of you! Jump upon this stone, as I did. We can then jump to the other side. Come now!"

"O mother! we can't, we can't, we can't!" said all the little chickens.

"Yes you can, if you try," said the old hen. "Just

flap your wings, as I did, and you can jump over."

"I am flapping my wings," said Chippy, who stood by himself; "but I can't jump any better than I could before."

chirped never   indeed
slowly   really
brood   began
didn't
use
door
bite
piece

"I never saw such children," said the old hen. "You don't try at all."

"We can't jump so far, mother. Indeed we can't, we can't!" chirped the little chickens.

"Well," said the old hen, "I must give it up." So she jumped back to the bank, and walked slowly home with her brood.

"I think mother asked too much of us," said one little chicken to the others.

"Well, I tried," said Chippy.

"We didn't," said the others; "it was of no use to try."

When they got home, the old hen began to look about for something to eat. She soon found, near the back door, a piece of bread.

So she called the chickens, and they all ran up to her, each one trying to get a bite at the piece of bread.

"No, no!" said the old hen. "This bread is for Chippy. He is the only one of my children that really tried to jump to the stone."

LESSON 115

last   slates   write   waste

neat   taken   clean   learn

reader   parents   second

We have come to the last lesson in this book. We have finished the First Reader.

You can now read all the lessons in it, and can write them on your slates.

Have you taken good care of your book? Children should always keep their books neat and clean.

Are you not glad to be ready for a new book?

Your parents are very kind to send you to school. If you are good, and if you try to learn, your teacher will love you, and you will please your parents.

Be kind to all, and do not waste your time in school. When you go home, you may ask your parents to get you a Second Reader.

SLATE EXERCISES

n   u   n   nun

u   r   n   urn

s   u   n   sun

c   o   w   cow

r   i   m   rim

c   a   t   cat

l   a   d   lad

b   o   x   box

h   e   n   hen

k   i   d   kid

q   u   o   quo

p   e   n   pen

j   a   r   jar

e   y   e   eye

g   u   n   gun

v   i   z   viz

i   v   y   ivy

f   a   n   fan

SCRIPT ALPHABET

$\mathcal{A}$ $\mathcal{B}$ $\mathcal{C}$ $\mathcal{D}$ $\mathcal{E}$ $\mathcal{F}$ $\mathcal{G}$

$\mathcal{H}$ $\mathcal{I}$ $\mathcal{J}$ $\mathcal{K}$ $\mathcal{L}$ $\mathcal{M}$ $\mathcal{N}$

$\mathcal{O}$ $\mathcal{P}$ $\mathcal{Q}$ $\mathcal{R}$ $\mathcal{S}$ $\mathcal{T}$ $\mathcal{U}$

$\mathcal{V}$ $\mathcal{W}$ $\mathcal{X}$ $\mathcal{Y}$ $\mathcal{Z}$

a b c d e f g h i

j k l m n o p q

r s t u v w x y z

SCRIPT FIGURES

1 2 3 4 5 6 7 8 9 0